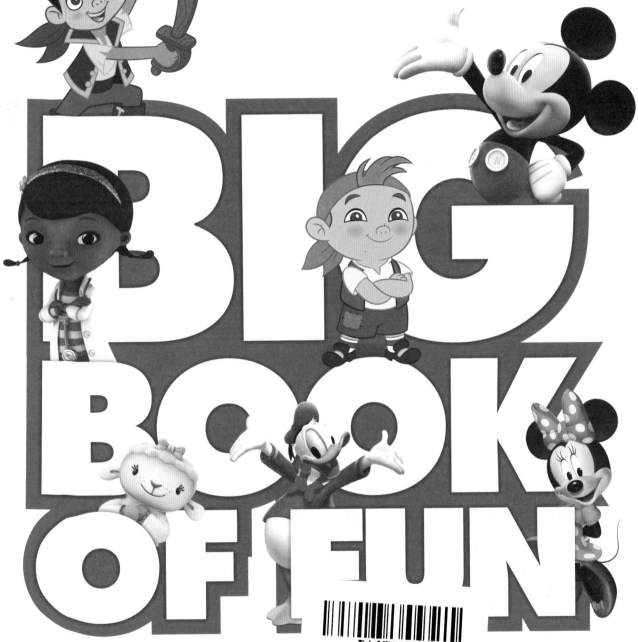

Disney Junior

BIG BOOK OF FUN

D1638095

Parragon

Bath • New York • Cologne • Melbourne • Delhi
Hong Kong • Shenzhen • Singapore • Amsterdam

This edition published by Parragon Books Ltd in 2014

Parragon Books Ltd
Chartist House
15–17 Trim Street
Bath BA1 1HA, UK
www.parragon.com

ISBN 978-1-4723-5620-8

Printed in China

Disney Junior

BIG BOOK OF FUN

Contents

MICKEY MOUSE CLUBHOUSE

UP, UP AND AWAY

By Sheila Sweeny Higginson
Illustrated by the Disney Storybook Artists
Designed by Elizabeth Andaluz

Donald and his friends were standing outside the Clubhouse on a crisp, bright day.

"Oh, Donald," Daisy said, "look at the sky! It's lovely!"

"Shhh!" Donald whispered. "Don't make a move! Something is following me and I'm going to find out who – or what – it is!"

Daisy giggled as she looked behind Donald. "Oh, my!" she said. "There is something following you! It's wearing a sailor's cap – just like yours. It's got cute webbed feet – just like yours. And when you move, it moves, too."

"Aw, phooey," Donald quacked as he turned around and saw ... his shadow! "That is a fine-looking shape, but I still don't trust it!"

Donald glared at his shadow.

"Cheer up, buddy," Mickey said. "Why don't you leave your shadow on the ground and come with me?"

"I don't know," Donald moped. "Where are we going?"

"Up, up and away!" Mickey cheered. "Who wants to help Minnie and me fly our hot-air balloon?"

"I sure do!" shouted Goofy.

"You can count me out," Donald grumbled. "I don't trust that thing. Besides," he added, "I'm not missing lunch."

"Aw, come on, Donald," Minnie pleaded. "I've packed a square meal for each of us. Up, up and away!"

Donald finally agreed to go with his friends.

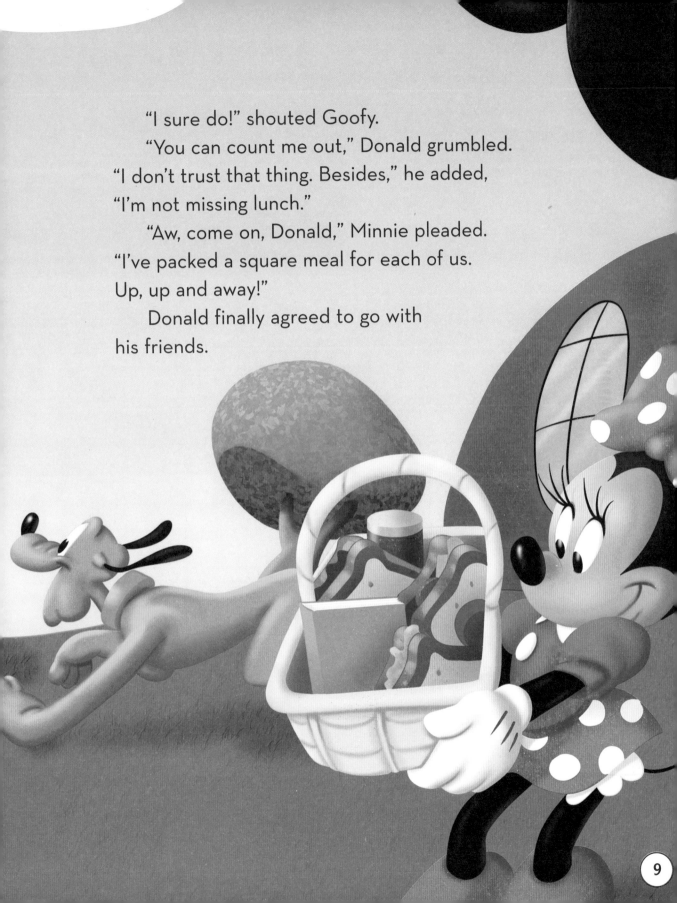

"Something's wrong," Mickey said. "The balloon won't fill with air!"

"That's too bad, buddy," said Donald, trying to hide a grin. "I guess we'll just have to go back to the Clubhouse for lunch."

"Oh, Toodles!" Mickey said. "Do we have a Mousketool that can help?" Toodles appeared. "Do any of you know how we can use this tool?" Mickey asked.

"I know, Mickey!" answered Minnie. "We can turn the handle to inflate the balloon with hot air."

"Why, you're right, Minnie!" Mickey shouted. "We've got ears! Say cheers!"

Soon, the friends were floating high above the Clubhouse.
"Up, up and away!" cried Daisy. "This is fun!"
"Look, everyone!" yelled Minnie. "Can you see the
Clubhouse from here? It looks so small! And there are so
many shapes below us. I see a heart and a rectangle.
What do you see?"

"I see a triangle!" Mickey said. "And there are Chip and Dale playing a round of golf!"

"It should be called a triangle of golf," laughed Daisy. "Just look at all those triangle-shaped flags!"

"What's a triangle?" asked Goofy, as he bit into his sandwich.

"A triangle is a shape with three sides that all have points at the ends – sort of like your sandwich," Minnie explained.

"Or like that?" Goofy questioned, as he pointed to a huge triangle in front of the balloon.

It was the top of a mountain! Suddenly, a gust of wind whisked the friends right towards it!

"We need help," cried Mickey. "Oh, Toodles!"

Toodles appeared with a triangle, a patch, a ladder and a spyglass.

"Which tool should we use?" asked Minnie.

"Let's try them all!" said Mickey. "Daisy, ring the triangle for help!" Daisy rang the triangle, but it didn't help them get off the mountain.

"Minnie, patch the hole!" cried Mickey. Minnie put a square patch on the round hole in the balloon, but it was too small.

"Goofy, look through the spyglass!" shouted Mickey. Goofy held the spyglass and saw that the ground looked very far away.

"There's only one tool left," yelled Mickey. "To the ladder!"

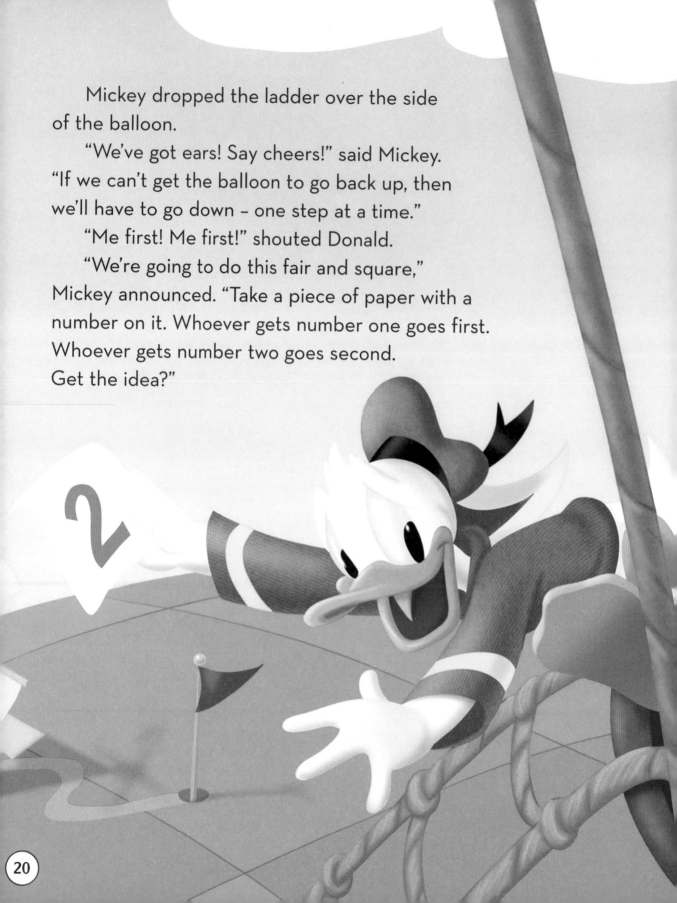

Mickey dropped the ladder over the side of the balloon.

"We've got ears! Say cheers!" said Mickey. "If we can't get the balloon to go back up, then we'll have to go down – one step at a time."

"Me first! Me first!" shouted Donald.

"We're going to do this fair and square," Mickey announced. "Take a piece of paper with a number on it. Whoever gets number one goes first. Whoever gets number two goes second. Get the idea?"

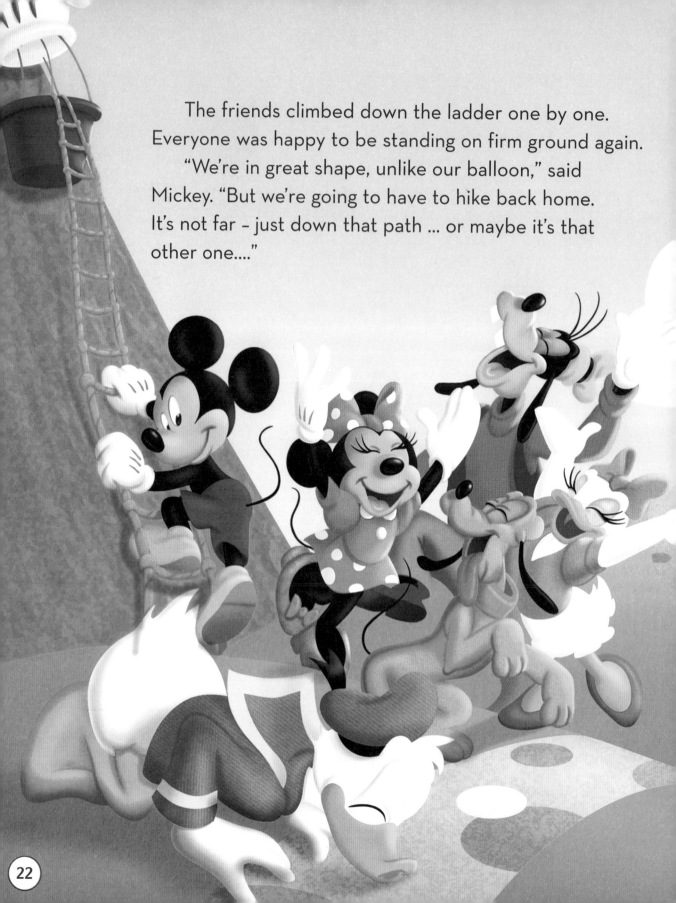

The friends climbed down the ladder one by one.
Everyone was happy to be standing on firm ground again.
"We're in great shape, unlike our balloon," said
Mickey. "But we're going to have to hike back home.
It's not far – just down that path ... or maybe it's that
other one...."

The friends trudged along, growing more and more tired.
"I think we've been walking in circles," Mickey finally said.
"I'm sure I've seen this tree before."

The friends needed help to get back to the Clubhouse. "Oh, Toodles!" Mickey called.

Toodles appeared, showing three pictures of Mickey. Mickey shared them with his friends:

"I'm standing in front of the Clubhouse and my shadow is different in each picture. In the morning, my shadow falls in front of me. At noon, I have no shadow. In the evening, my shadow falls behind me. Do any of you know what this could mean?"

The friends looked at the pictures carefully.
"I've got it!" Donald shouted. "Right now, it's late
and the sun is setting behind us. Toodles shows that in
the evening, our shadows point towards the Clubhouse.
If we follow them, they'll lead us back home."

Donald was right! The shadows helped the friends walk in the right direction. Soon, they arrived back at the Clubhouse. Everyone was hungry from the long trip.

"Well, Donald," Daisy said, "do you trust your shadow now?"

"I'll trust the handsome guy to lead me home," Donald answered. "But he better not ask me to share my pie!"

The End

Bubble Trouble

Based on the episode written by Kurt Redeker
Adapted by Sheila Sweeny Higginson
Illustrated by Alan Batson

Doc likes to play with her best friend Emmie and her little sister Alma.

One of their favourite toys is a Bubble Monkey bubble blower.

Emmie puts Bubble Monkey on the picnic
table and flips her switch. One, two, three ...

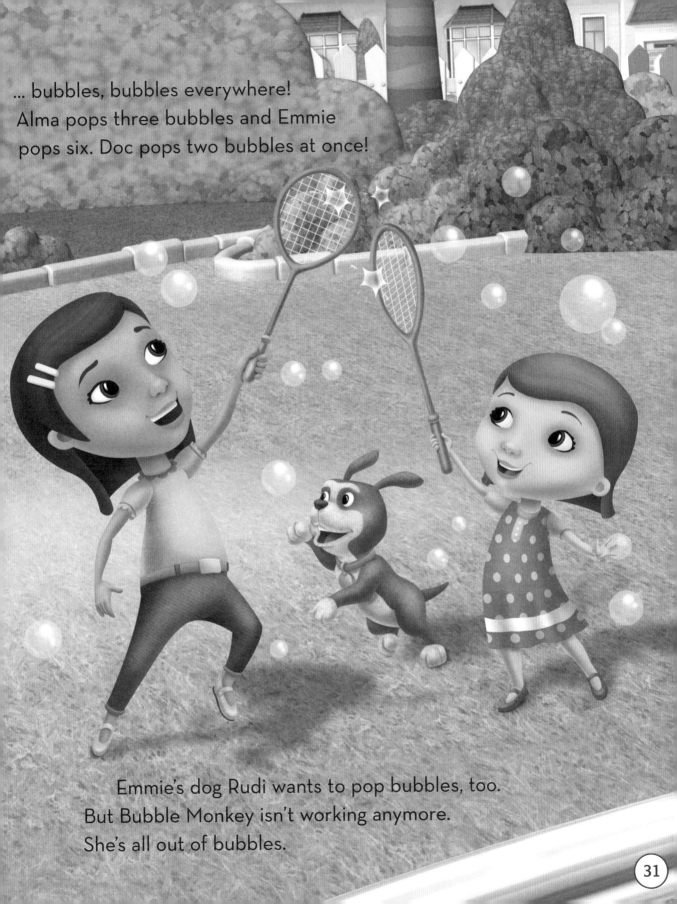

... bubbles, bubbles everywhere!
Alma pops three bubbles and Emmie
pops six. Doc pops two bubbles at once!

Emmie's dog Rudi wants to pop bubbles, too.
But Bubble Monkey isn't working anymore.
She's all out of bubbles.

Alma fills up Bubble Monkey while Doc and Emmie chase after Rudi. She asks, "Is everyone ready?"
They are!

One two, three – but no bubbles!

"Where are the bubbles?" asks Alma.
"I'll take a look and see if I can figure out what's wrong," says Doc.

Doc takes Bubble Monkey to her clinic and brings her to life with her magic stethoscope.

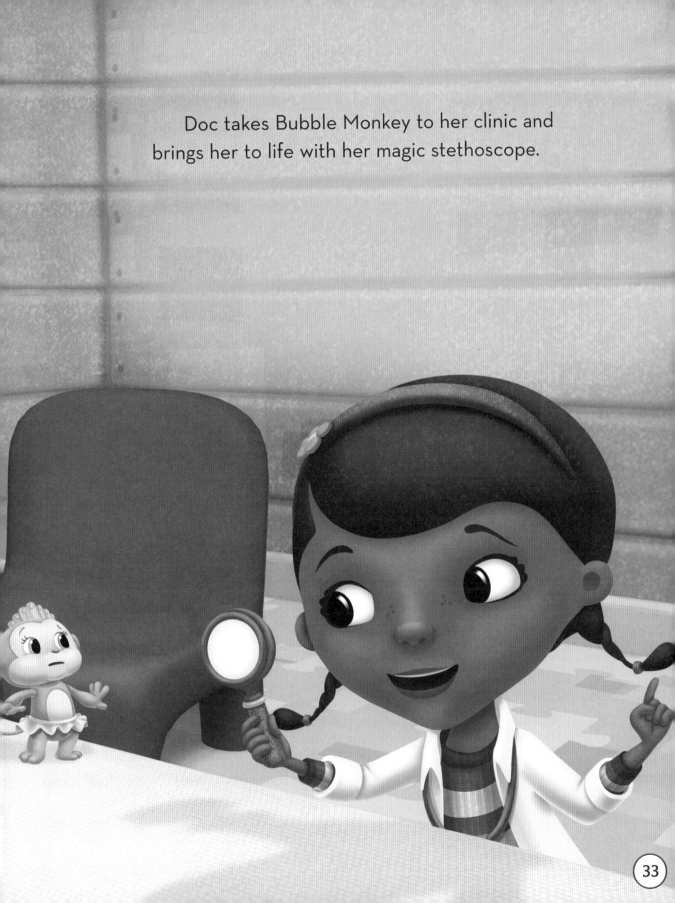

First, Doc runs some tests and takes a feather from her bag. She asks Bubble Monkey to blow the feather. Bubble Monkey blows, but it barely moves.

Next, Doc listens to Bubble Monkey's chest.
"Sounds like goop is blocking your bubble pumper," she says.
"Are you having any other symptoms?"
"Well, I have a tummy ache," Bubble Monkey says.

"Can I give your tummy a little squeeze?" Doc asks.
She presses Bubble Monkey's stomach. Something shoots
out and hits Stuffy in the chest. "Ick!" says Stuffy.

Now Stuffy and Chilly are stuck together!
"Weird," says Doc as she pulls them apart. "This is glue."

Doc heads back to Emmie's garden to investigate.

"Alma, what did you put in Bubble Monkey?" she asks.

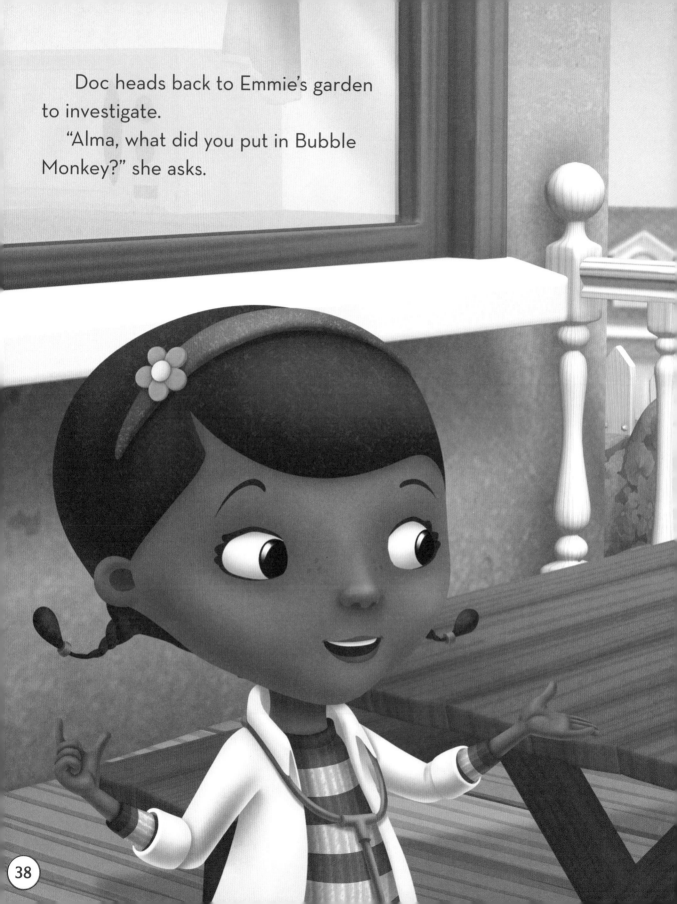

Alma holds up the pink jar. "I used this," she says.
"Alma, the pink one is glue!" Emmie says. "The green
one is the bubble soap!"

Doc rushes back to the clinic.

"I have a diagnosis!" she tells Bubble Monkey. "You have a bad case of Gunk-inside-atude."

"Toys need to get filled right, just like people need to eat right," says Doc.

Then Doc cleans out Bubble Monkey's tubes and fills her up with bubble soap.

"Thanks, Doc. I feel better! You're super fantastic!"
Bubble Monkey cheers.

"I love my job!" says Doc. "Now let's get you back to Emmie and Alma."

"I'm back!" Doc says. "And this time, I brought Bubble Monkey!"

"Did you fix her?" Alma asks.
"There's only one way to find out," says Doc.
   One ... two ... three ...

MICKEY MOUSE CLUBHOUSE

FUN ACTIVITIES!

Hi, there! Do you want to come to my clubhouse?
Just colour me in and say 'Meeska, Mooska, Mickey Mouse!'

Here it is – the Clubhouse! Colour it in and come on inside!

Colour this picture of the kitchen. It has an oven, a sink and a … leaping frog! Hey, what's he doing here?

Let's follow the leaping frog to the garden. How many bees do you see in the picture? Circle the number.

1 2 3 4 5 6 7 8 9 10

Pluto and the frog are playing a game. It's called 'leapfrog'.
Who is hopping higher? Colour them in.

Can you help Pluto find the frog in this picture?
Then colour it in.

Daisy has found the frog!
Colour this picture of the frog in her basket.

Match the leaping frog to its shadow.

Come on back to the Clubhouse. It looks like Daisy needs help getting ready for a surprise party! Colour this picture.

Daisy and Mickey blew up all of these balloons!
Find two that are exactly the same and colour them in!

Answer:

Daisy is baking a cake. How many eggs is she using?
Circle the number.

1 2 3 4 5 6 7 8 9 10

The cake is finished! You can help to decorate it.
Draw two candles on top of the cake.

It is time for some ice cream! Draw two scoops
in Minnie's cone, then colour in the picture.

Now Daisy and Donald are sharing a banana split.
How many spoons are in the picture?

'Pin the Tail on the Donkey' is Goofy's favourite party game.
He is trying to put the tail in the right place.

Now it's your turn! Draw a tail on this donkey.

It's getting late and the guests are leaving the party. Oh, Toodles!
Which of these objects will help them to find their way in the dark?
Point to the correct object.

Who has Donald found hiding on the path?

It's time for an out-of-this-world adventure! Colour this picture of Goofy blasting off to outer space! Go, Goofy!

Help Goofy get to Mars – draw a path through the maze.

Answer:

How many planets are in Goofy's path?
Circle the number, then colour in the picture.

1 2 3 4 5 6 7 8 9 10

Three of these spaceships look the same.
Goofy's spaceship is different. Can you find Goofy's ship?

Answer:

Goofy needs help getting down from his spaceship.
Which Mouseketool should he use? Point to the correct object.

Goofy has invited four aliens back to the Clubhouse!
Colour this picture of Goofy and his new friends.

Draw a line to match each alien to its shadow.

Answer:

Welcome to the Clubhouse garden! Colour this picture
of Minnie and Daisy doing some gardening.

Minnie has taken some photographs of the garden.
How many pictures are there? Circle the number.

1 2 3 4 5 6 7 8 9 10

Minnie is picking some flowers to make a bunch.

Help her by colouring in the flowers.

Colour in this picture of Daisy making a flower chain!

Can you find one tree, two sunflowers, three birds, four bees and five friends in this picture? Circle them as you find them.

Answer:

Draw a line to match each picture with the correct number.

1

2

3

4

5

Answer:

We're having a great day at the zoo! Write the number to show how many legs each animal has on the ground.

Answer:

Write the numbers one to five to put these zoo animals
in size order, from smallest to biggest.

___

___

___

___

___

The seal pond is Pluto's favourite place at the zoo.
The seals are throwing balls.

The monkeys are swinging from the branches.

Draw a line to match each animal to its shadow.

83

Help Goofy through the maze to find his way to the penguins.

What a great day! Now I want to read a book.
Colour in Mickey's story time.

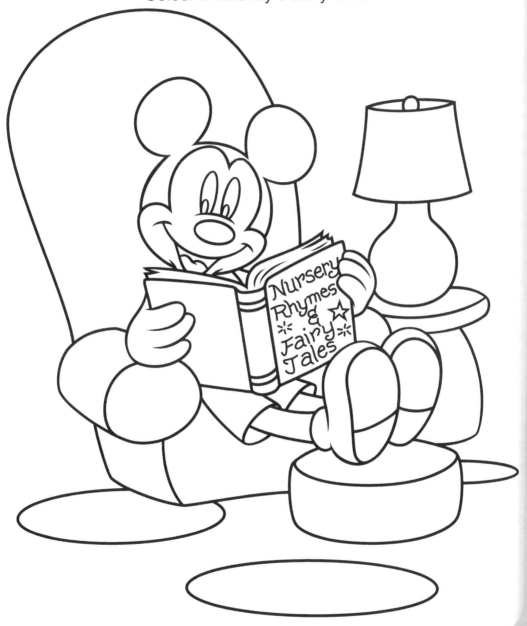

It's bedtime! That means it's time for me to put my book away.

TREASURE HUNT
ACTIVITIES

Join Jake's pirate crew – draw yourself as a pirate.

Remember to add these pirate items.

spyglass	eye patch
compass	sword
coin purse	pirate hat

Now that you're part of the pirate crew,
it's time to go to Pirate Island!
Which line on the map leads to Pirate Island?
Remember: 'X' marks the spot!

Answer:

There's one thing every pirate crew needs ... a hideout!
Look at the two pictures of the hideout.
Find and circle five differences.

Colour in a skull and crossbones every time you find a difference.

Answer:

You're up in the hideout crow's nest with Jake.
Which of these ships is the Jolly Roger? Circle it and say,
"The Jolly Roger be heading this way!"

1

2

3

Answer:

How many times can you find the word PIRATE in this wordsearch? Circle the words as you find them.

X	M	Y	N	O	P	E	P
P	P	I	R	A	T	E	I
I	O	I	B	A	I	I	R
R	U	X	R	R	W	R	A
A	R	U	T	A	O	Q	T
T	P	P	I	R	A	T	E
E	E	E	R	A	K	L	Y
P	I	R	A	T	E	I	N

Answer: 5

How many Gold Doubloons has the pirate crew earned?
Count them!

Answer:

9

Colour in the sneaky snook, Captain Hook!

Yo-ho, way to go!
Colour in Jake, Izzy, Cubby and Skully.

Draw a line to match the pirates to their property.

Answer:

All shipshape and seaworthy pirates have their own skull and crossbones.

This is Jake's:

This is Captain Hook's:

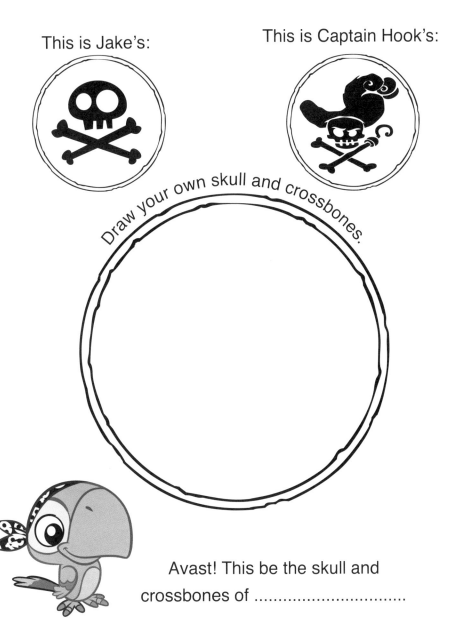

Draw your own skull and crossbones.

Avast! This be the skull and crossbones of ....

Shiver me timbers! Captain Hook is trying to spy on Jake and his pirate crew. Colour in the pesky pirate.

Jake has noticed that something odd has washed
up on the beach....

Look at the two pictures below – can you spy the difference?

Jake and his crew want to return Hook's hat to him
because it's the right thing to do.
Can you guide Bucky and the pirate crew through
the maze to the Jolly Roger?

Colour in this spyglass
and keep a lookout!

Where's the best place
to be on the lookout?
C _ _ _ ' _ N _ _ _ .

The Jolly Roger has been spotted near Skull Rock. Let's check Cubby's map. Can you circle Skull Rock?

Can you point to the four points of the compass?

What's that sound? It's Tick Tock Croc! Colour him in!

Help Jake climb up the rope net to get aboard the Jolly Roger.
Use the key to move through the maze.

Key:

Move Left

Move Up

Finish

Start

Answer:

Hook is happy to have his hat back, but he wishes those scallywags hadn't had so much fun returning it! Join the dots and colour in Captain Hook's hat.

It's Skully's birthday and Jake, Izzy and Cubby are
throwing him a party.
Draw a present for Skully below.

Look at the picture of Skully's party
and answer the questions below.

1. How many party hats can you count? _____

2. Circle the correct sentence.

Jake is wearing a headscarf.　　Jake is wearing a neckscarf.

3. Who has a bag of pixie dust around her neck? _____

4. Jake, Izzy and Cubby are children. Skully is a _____ .

In the boxes below, write your own pirate adventure and draw pictures to match. The first story box has been done for you.

1. It's Skully's birthday. Jake and the crew have planned a party. But, oh no! Captain Hook has stolen all of Skully's presents!

2.

3.

Hints and tips:
- Make sure your story has a beginning, a middle and an end.
- Who are the characters in your story?
- Where is the story taking place?
- What is happening in your story?

Remember: there's no limit to your imagination, so get creative!

4. _____

_____

5. _____

_____

6. _____

_____

Take it in turns with a friend to connect two of the dots
with a line. If your line completes a square, put your initial in it.
Continue until all the dots are joined up. The player
with the most boxes is the winner!

Grab a piratey friend and decide which of you is going to be Jake and which of you is going to be Hook. Take it in turns to draw either a sword (for Jake) and a hook (for Hook). The first player to get three in a row is the winner!

Captain Hook and Mr Smee have taken Skully's presents up to Shipwreck Rock. How will Jake and the crew rescue them?

Cross out every 'A' to discover the answer and copy the remaining letters onto the lines below.

AFAALAY WAAIATAH IAAZAZAAYAAS PAIAAXAIAE ADUASAAT

_ _ _   _ _ _ _   _ _ _ _ _ ,

_ _ _ _ _   _ _ _ .

Answer: FLY WITH IZZY'S PIXIE DUST.

110

Hooray! The pirate crew can finally have a party for Skully!
Complete the party by giving everyone a party hat,
then colour them in!

Jake's sword was given to him by Peter Pan
so he could be a good leader. Are you a good leader, too?
Draw your pirate sword below.

Oh, no! That sneaky snook Captain Hook has stolen Jake's sword. Can you find it below?

Answer:

Jake and the crew are chasing after Captain Hook and
Mr Smee because they've stolen Jake's sword. Guide Jake
through the maze to get his sword back.

Answer:

Jake and the pirate crew have followed Captain Hook to a canyon, but Hook has pushed the log bridge into the canyon, so they can't cross. Izzy has a plan ... they can use her pixie dust and fly over!

1. Which of these pictures shows Izzy using her pixie dust? _____

1.

2.

3.

4.

Read these sentences. Are they true or false? Circle the answer.

2. Izzy is in every picture.

    true   false

3. Skully is flying in all the pictures.

    true   false

Hook is trying to open a mysterious door using Jake's sword as a key. Which shape will Jake's sword fit into?

1.

2.

3.

4.

Answer: 4

In each section, circle your favourite and find
out which pirate you are most like.

1. Possession

a. sword

b. map

c. pixie dust

d. Captain
Hook's hat

2. Hobby

a. sailing

b. playing harmonica

c. flying

d. napping

3. Catchphrase

a. "Yo, ho! Let's go!"

b. "Aw, coconuts!"

c. "Shiver me timbers!"

d. "I never have any fun!"

Mostly a
You're most like Jake. You're the leader
of the crew and always include your best
friends in the fun.

Mostly c
You're most like Izzy. You are full of
ideas and you always think things
through carefully.

Mostly b
You're most like Cubby. You're always
rarin' to go-go-GO! You always overcome
your fears and act bravely.

Mostly d
Oh dear, you're most like Captain Hook.
You're a sneaky snook, who doesn't like to
see other people have fun.

At the door, the crew find a message from Peter Pan:
"Only a great leader can open this door, with an enchanted sword and nothing more."
Look at the clues and write the answers in the grid.
The name of the person who can open the door will appear in the yellow boxes.

1. _ _ _ _ _ Roger.

2. _ _ _ .

3. _ _ _ _ _ .

4. Crow's
_ _ _ _ .

Count the Gold Doubloons and colour them in.

Saying what you want to say, but in a pirate way!

Circle the pirate phrases below.

"Welcome aboard, me hearties!"

"I don't like treasure."

"Anchors aweigh!"

"Shiver me timbers!"

"I always get sea-sick!"

"Arrrggh! Fill me boots with barnacles!"

Answers: "Welcome aboard, me hearties!"; "Anchors aweigh!"; "Shiver me timbers!"; "Arrrggh! Fill me boots with barnacles!"

The Never Land pirates are dancing to a rocking sea shanty.
Colour them in.

Make your own pirate song by circling the words at the end of each verse that you like the most.

On the shores of Never Land,
There's a pirate crew   *you know* / *yo ho!*

For new adventures, they set sail,
Yo ho!   *Let's go* / *Let's row!*

Hook, he wants to spoil the fun,
Hear him cry,   *"Avast!"* / *"The last!"*

Jake's pirate crew have fun in the sun,
Every day is such   *a blast!* / *a laugh!*

Hook has spotted who is making the noise through his spyglass.
How many music notes can you count?

Answer:

20

Oh, no! Captain Hook and Mr Smee have stolen Cubby's drums.
Help Jake and the pirate crew follow the music
notes to the sneaky pirates.

These two pirates love to burst into song at the drop of a gang plank. Circle five differences between the two pictures.

Answer:

Join the dots to complete the map of Never Land.

Draw a line and match each pirate to their shadow.

Complete this dot-to-dot of the pirate ship and colour it in.

Look at this picture of Captain Hook and Smee.
Find and circle six differences between the two pictures.
Hint: In each grid square, there is one difference.

Answer:

What are Jake, Izzy, Cubby and Skully saying?
Can you trace over the letters to find out?

There's a spooky myth about the golden pumpkin.
The words on the end of each line rhyme.
Circle the rhyming word to complete the myth.

On Halloween eve, the golden pumpkin rises up **high**,
In the Never Land **sky/clouds**,
And it starts to **fly/float**.

Can you circle some other words that rhyme with 'high'?

pie   **pirate**

boots   **by**

try   **ship**

Which of these shells belongs to Izzy?

Hint: It is different to all the others.

1

2

3

4

5

Answer:

5

Activity Adventures!

Ellyvan has come to play football. Oh dear, no one else is here!
Colour this picture of Ellyvan and the empty pitch.

Taxicrab is making smoothies for his friends. They have just finished a game of football. But where was Ellyvan?

Find the path that leads to the goal.

Answer:

Oh, dear! Ellyvan missed the game. Colour him in.

Colour this picture of Bungo telling Ellyvan about
the goal he scored to win the game.

Tomorrow is the day for the big Coconut Run Road Race.
"Don't be late, Ellyvan!" says Taxicrab.

Can you help Bungo and Dozer fill the holes in the road?
Draw lines to connect the right shapes to the right holes.

Answer:

Zoom! The Coconut Run Road Race is underway!

Toadhog and Zooter are nearly at the finish line!

Zooter wins! Join the dots to complete the picture.

Colour this picture of Zooter receiving the trophy!
Hooray for Zooter!

Miss Jolly and the Beetlebugs are going to check on Ellyvan. He missed the race!

How many Beetlebugs can you count?

Write your answer in the circle.

Answer: 8

"I went to the starting line but no one else was there," says Ellyvan. "So I came home."

"You were too early!" says Miss Jolly. "The race was in the afternoon, not the morning."

Bungo has made signs to help Ellyvan learn the parts of the day.
Help Ellyvan by numbering the signs in this order –
1. Morning, 2. Afternoon, 3. Night.

Answer:

Morning is when Ellyvan eats his breakfast of cereal and fruit.

"Afternoon starts with lunchtime and goes all the way to suppertime," says Bungo.

Can you match these friends to their shadows?

Answer:

"The picnic is tomorrow afternoon, Ellyvan,"
says Hippobus. "Don't forget!"

The next day, Ellyvan is on time for the picnic!
But where is everyone else?

Eight of Ellyvan's friends are hiding in this picture.

Can you find them?

Answer:

Colour this picture of everyone jumping out to surprise Ellyvan. "You're right on time!" they shout.

"Hooray!" says Ellyvan. "I was hungry!" What a wonderful picnic!

Toadhog is up on the roof fixing his weathervane.

The Beetlebugs are going on a field trip.
Careful! There's a bumpy road ahead!

Which picture of Miss Jolly is different to the others?

A.

B.

C.

D.

Answer:

B

Can you help Miss Jolly find the way to Toadhog's house? The road signs will help you.

Whoops! Toadhog slipped. He is falling into the river!

Toadhog's Trouble

Written by Melinda LaRose
Illustrated by Alan Batson

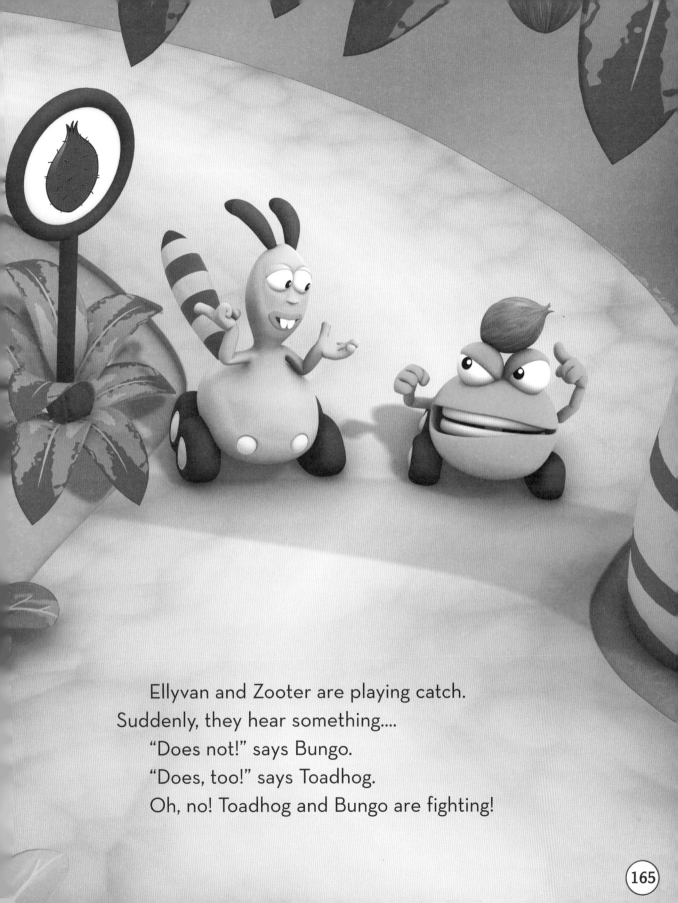

Ellyvan and Zooter are playing catch.
Suddenly, they hear something....
"Does not!" says Bungo.
"Does, too!" says Toadhog.
Oh, no! Toadhog and Bungo are fighting!

Toadhog got lost going to the mud pond!
"This sign points to the mud pond!"
says Toadhog.

"It does not," says Bungo. "That sign is for the Coconut Grove."

"Bungo, your signs are silly!" shouts Toadhog.

Bungo takes his sign and rolls away.

"Toadhog!" says Zooter. "That wasn't very nice.
You hurt Bungo's feelings."
"Maybe you should say you're sorry," says Ellyvan.
"Harrumph!" says Toadhog.

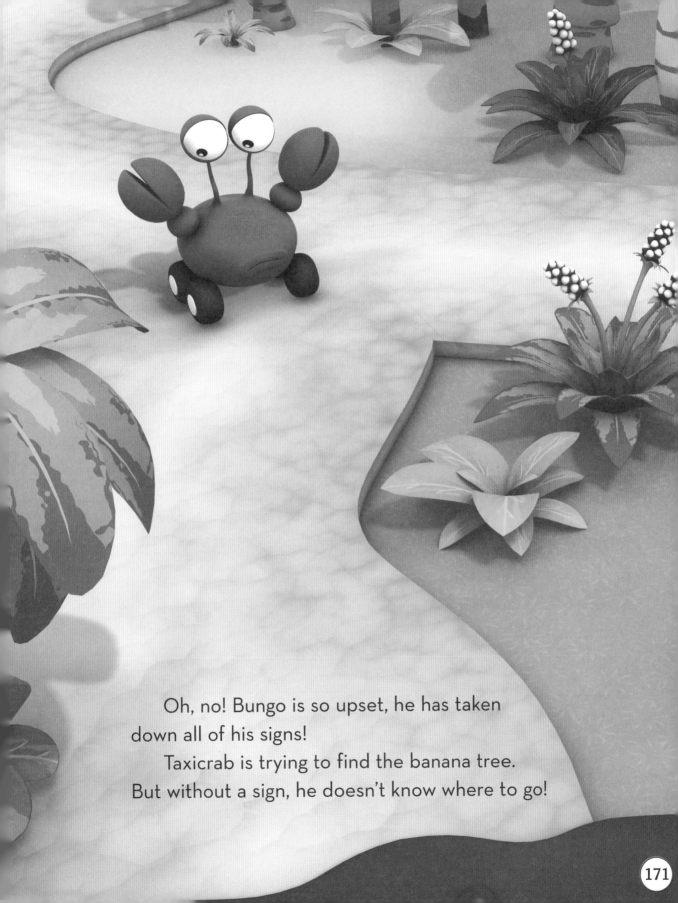

Oh, no! Bungo is so upset, he has taken
down all of his signs!
Taxicrab is trying to find the banana tree.
But without a sign, he doesn't know where to go!

Not that way Taxicrab!

Splash!

Hippobus is driving the Beetlebugs to school.
"Hmm, which way do I go?" she wonders.

Whoa!
Not that way!

"I don't need Bungo's silly signs," says
Toadhog. "I can find the mud pond myself."
Not that way! **Buzzzz!**

"Have you seen Hippobus?" asks Miss Jolly.
"The Beetlebugs are not at school!"

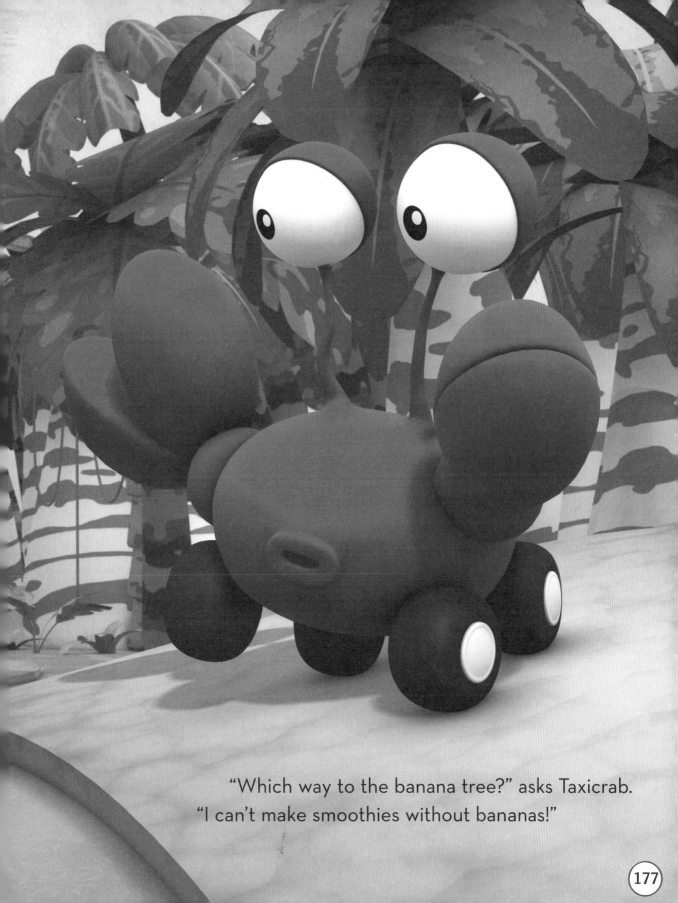

"Which way to the banana tree?" asks Taxicrab.
"I can't make smoothies without bananas!"

Suddenly, Toadhog races by. He's being chased by a swarm of bees!

"Ahh!" cries Toadhog.

"Oh, dear," says Zooter. "We need Bungo's signs!"

"Toadhog, you have to apologize to Bungo," says Ellyvan.
"All right, all right," says Toadhog.

Zooter, Ellyvan and Toadhog go to Bungo's warren.
"Bungo, you make the best signs in Jungle Junction,"
says Toadhog. "And ... I got lost without them. I'm sorry."
"Well, okay," Bungo says with a smile.

Toadhog helps Bungo put back all of
the signs around the jungle.

And as the sun sets on Jungle Junction, the two friends enjoy banana smoothies and a nice mud bath!

The End

FOLLOW THAT SOUND!

WRITTEN BY **MELINDA LA ROSE**

ILLUSTRATED BY **ALAN BATSON**

One day on Shipwreck Beach, Cubby is playing his harmonica.

"Aw, coconuts! I'll never be ready in time to play at Marina's party," says Cubby sadly.

Hook is drifting off to sleep in his hammock, when suddenly he is startled awake by the sound of music!

"One of those puny pirates is making an awful racket with his blowy music thing!" says Hook.

"Why don't you ask the sea pups nicely if they'll be a little quieter?" says Smee.

"Smee, who do you think you're dealing with?" says Hook. "Why would I ask nicely when I can take the blowy thing away!"

Hook uses his fishing hook to nab the harmonica right out
of Cubby's mouth!

Swoosh!

"My harmonica!" says Cubby.
"We gotta get it back!" says Jake.

Smee blows into the harmonica. It makes a terrible noise!

Weeeee-yooouuu!

Startled, Smee throws the harmonica up in the air ...
but it doesn't come back down!

"Um, Cap'n," says Smee, "the
harmonica just disappeared!"

"Crackers!" says Skully. "That monkey took the harmonica!"

"He's heading for the Never Jungle," says Cubby.

"Come on, crew," says Jake. "Follow that monkey!"

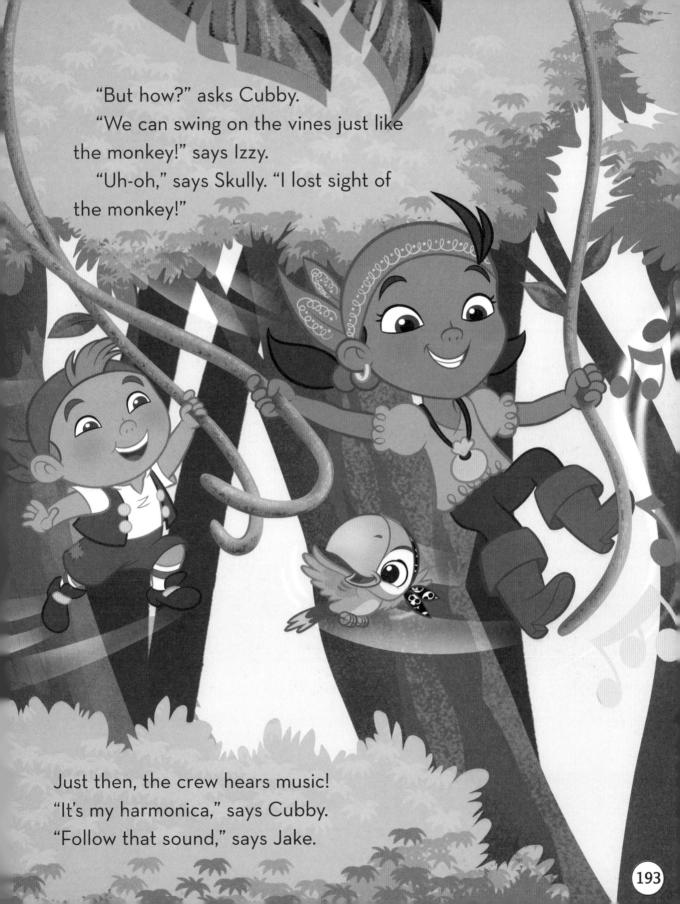

"But how?" asks Cubby.

"We can swing on the vines just like the monkey!" says Izzy.

"Uh-oh," says Skully. "I lost sight of the monkey!"

Just then, the crew hears music!

"It's my harmonica," says Cubby.

"Follow that sound," says Jake.

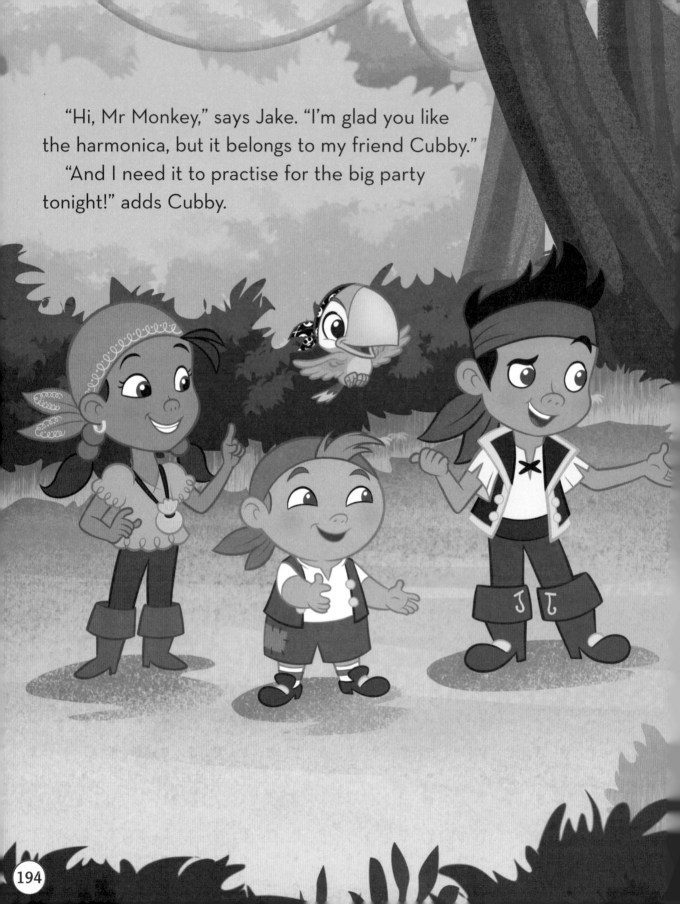

"Hi, Mr Monkey," says Jake. "I'm glad you like the harmonica, but it belongs to my friend Cubby."
"And I need it to practise for the big party tonight!" adds Cubby.

"He doesn't want to give the harmonica back," says Izzy.
"If only we had another instrument," says Jake.
"Then we could trade with the monkey."
"That's a great idea," says Izzy.

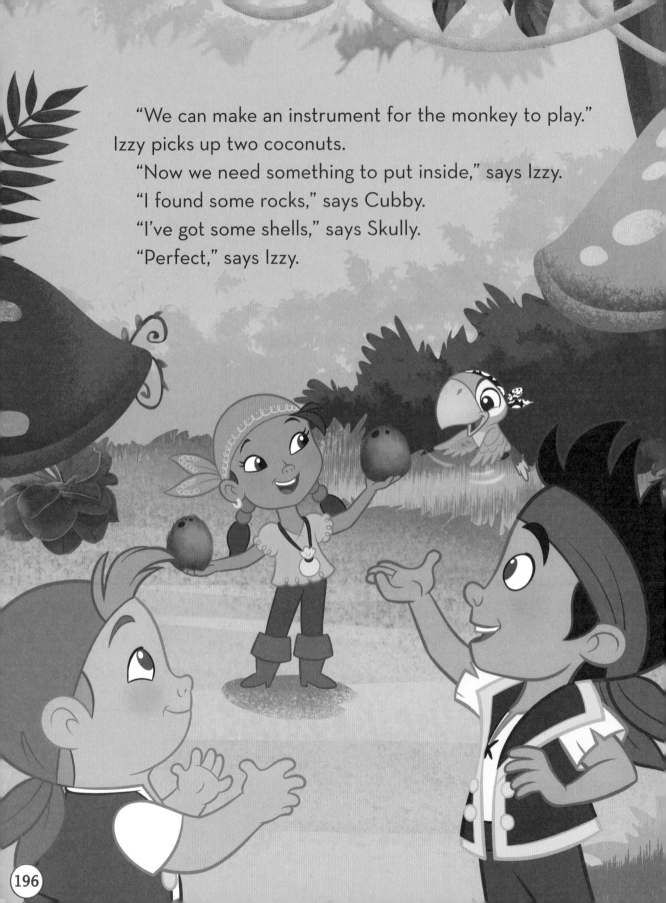

"We can make an instrument for the monkey to play."
Izzy picks up two coconuts.

"Now we need something to put inside," says Izzy.

"I found some rocks," says Cubby.

"I've got some shells," says Skully.

"Perfect," says Izzy.

"Awesome! You made maracas for the monkey," says Jake. The monkey gives Cubby back his harmonica.

"Thanks!" says Cubby. "Hey, do you wanna come back to Shipwreck Beach and jam with me?"

"Oo-oo-oo," says the happy monkey.

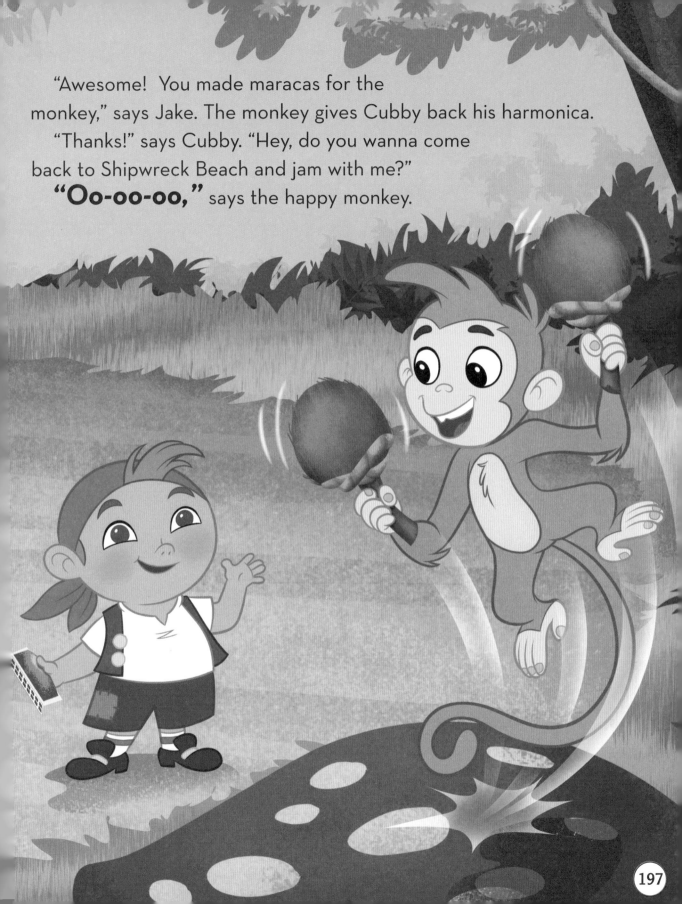

197

Cubby and the monkey play music together
on the beach!

"Blast it, now there's twice as much racket!"
says Captain Hook.

"What's the matter?" asks Jake.

"The Cap'n can't have his nappy-nap, what with all that music," says Smee.

"Why didn't you just ask us to be quieter?" asks Jake.

"But, how can I practise for the party?" says Cubby.

"I've got an idea," says Jake.

Cubby and the monkey play a gentle lullaby for Captain Hook. Mr Smee sings:

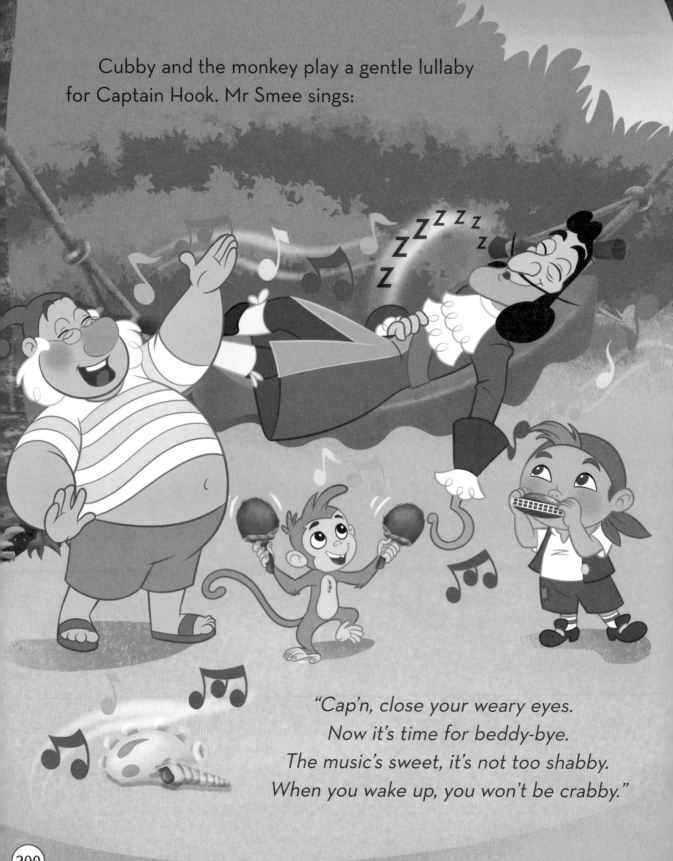

"Cap'n, close your weary eyes.
Now it's time for beddy-bye.
The music's sweet, it's not too shabby.
When you wake up, you won't be crabby."

Hook falls asleep and starts to snore!

"We'd better get ready for the party," says Jake.

"What? I can't hear you over all that noise," says Skully.

Later that night, Cubby and the monkey play their instruments at Marina's party!

"Cubby, thank you so much for playing," says Marina. "You were amazing!"

"You're welcome," says Cubby, blushing.

"Yo-ho, way to go!" says Jake. "See? All that practising paid off!"

"Can't you hear it, Smee," says Captain Hook.

"Hear what, Cap'n?" asks Smee.

"That blasted lullaby. I can't get it out of me head," says Hook.

"Oh, dear, you're imagining things, Cap'n," says Smee.

"I guess I am," says Hook.

"I can see why. It was a catchy tune, if I do say so myself," says Smee. "And the lyrics were top-notch."

Uh-oh! The monkey has stowed away on the *Jolly Roger*!

"If Hook had just asked us to be quiet, we wouldn't have gone through all that trouble today," says Jake.

"Yeah, Hook should know better! If you need something, you should ask nicely," says Izzy.

"Yeah, but if the monkey didn't take the harmonica, we never would've gotten to jam together!" says Cubby.

The End

Colour in your favourite instrument below,
then draw yourself in a pirate band with Cubby.